I Love When Daddy Reads to Me!

by Patrick Patterson

with Peyton and Lorin Patterson

art by V. Kuroji Patrick with Jerry Craft

Two Little Publishers • Raleigh

I Love When Daddy Reads to Me!
Written by Patrick Patterson with Peyton and Lorin Patterson
Illustrated by V. Kuroji Patrick with Jerry Craft
Book Design by Jerry Craft

Visit us on the web at
www.twolittlepublishers.com
Email: globalpartners202@gmail.com

Follow on Twitter @patrickpat803

Summary: "I Love When Daddy Reads to Me" is a fun and engaging children's book that encourages Father/Child Bonding & Literacy! This book is unique in that it encourages Dads to read to their children and shares many of the funny and loving reasons why, from a child's perspective!

ISBN-10: 0-692-76235-3

ISBN-13: 978-0-692-76235-6

First Edition
Printed in the United States

Published by Two Little Publishers

This book is dedicated to James "Pat" Patterson, Jr. and Aubrey Gene Ashford, Sr, the fathers of Patrick and Sherani (Ashford) Patterson, and grandfathers of Peyton and Lorin. These men sacrificed, demonstrated love, and created memories with their most precious gift to their families, their Time.

I **Love** when Daddy reads to me
because we get **ALL** of
his attention.

I **Love** when Daddy reads to me because he's **SoOoo** funny!

I **Love** when Daddy reads to me because we can ask him all kinds of questions...

...and because we get to learn
new things togetHer.

I **Love** when Daddy reads to me because I **Love** how he makes the animals sound real...

...and because he lets **US** make animal noises too!

I **L**o**v**e when Daddy reads
to me because...

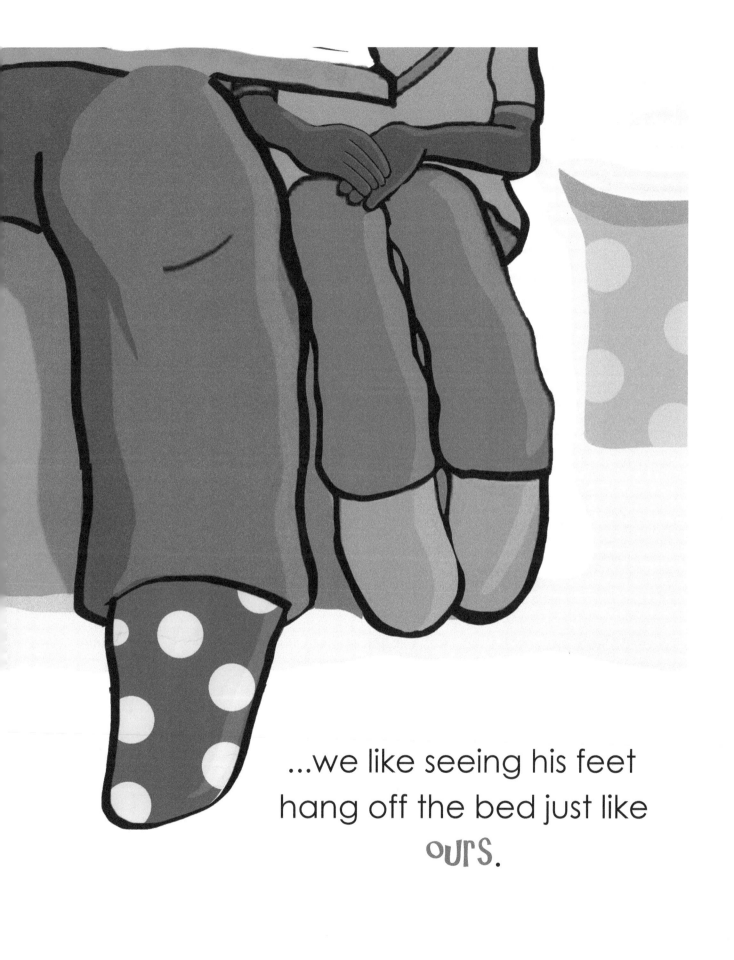

...we like seeing his feet hang off the bed just like ours.

I LOVe when Daddy reads to me...

...because it makes us feel SaFe
when he's home.

I **Love** when Daddy reads to me...

...because it makes Mommy SMiLe really BIG!

I **LOVe** when Daddy reads to me...

...because it makes **M**e
want to read too!

PATRICK PATTERSON

Patrick J. Patterson, MSW, MPH is Manager of President Obama's *National Responsible Fatherhood Clearinghouse* in Washington, DC. He manages an 11 million dollar budget and project that provides oversight, training and technical assistance to federally funded fatherhood programs nationally. These programs provide services that connect and strengthen the relationship between fathers, their children and families.

As a national fatherhood leader and speaker, Patrick has effectively delivered more than 750 fatherhood trainings, keynotes, consultations and workshops with public/ private agencies in 42 states, the US Virgin Islands and 4 countries.

In 2014, the *National Partnership for Community Leadership* (NPCL) awarded the prestigious "International Fatherhood Practitioner of the Year" to Patrick for the impact of his fatherhood work globally. He is also an *NFL Players Association* consultant where he trains current and former NFL players with fatherhood, parenting and healthy relationship skills.

He earned a Bachelor of Social Work degree from Benedict College (Columbia, SC) and dual Masters degrees in Social Work and Public Health from the University of South Carolina.

He is married to his high school sweetheart, Sherani Ashford Patterson, and they have two beautiful daughters, Peyton and Lorin (who helped to write this book).

CPSIA information can be obtained
at www.ICGtesting.com
Printed in the USA
BVHW020926090520
579314BV00011B/915